Contents

Some words are printed in bold, **like this**. You can find out what they mean in the glossary. You can also look in the box at the bottom of the page where the word first appears.

Explore The Titanic With Robert Ballard

The passenger liner *Titanic* hit an iceberg on 14 April 1912. It happened around midnight. In less than three hours, the *Titanic* sank into the deep, icy ocean. Sadly, 1,523 people drowned.

Finding *Titanic*

No one knew where the *Titanic* had gone down. Seventy-three years later, US explorer Robert Ballard searched the ocean floor. He used special cameras. On 1 September 1985, he spotted the *Titanic*. Ballard later explored the wreck in a small **submarine** (underwater ship).

iceberg	huge chunk of ice floating in the ocean
passenger liner	ship built to carry people
submarine	special ship built to go underwater

ATOMIC

EXPLORERS

Elizabeth Raum

www.raintreepublishers.co.uk

Visit our website to find out more information about **Raintree** books.

To order:
☎ Phone 44 (0) 1865 888112
▤ Send a fax to 44 (0) 1865 314091
▯ Visit the Raintree bookshop at **www.raintreepublishers.co.uk** to browse our catalogue and order online.

First published in Great Britain by
Raintree, Halley Court, Jordan Hill,
Oxford OX2 8EJ, part of Harcourt
Education. Raintree is a registered
trademark of Harcourt Education Ltd.

Editorial: Louise Galpine and Catherine Clarke
Design: Victoria Bevan and Bigtop
Picture research: Hannah Taylor
Illustrations: Jeff Edwards and Darren Lingard
Production: Julie Carter

Originated by Chroma Graphics Pte. Ltd
Printed and bound in China by Leo Paper Group

ISBN: 978 1 4062 0673 9 (hardback)
12 11 10 09 08
10 9 8 7 6 5 4 3 2 1

ISBN: 978 1 4062 0694 4 (paperback)
13 12 11 10 09
10 9 8 7 6 5 4 3 2 1

British Library
Cataloguing in Publication Data
Raum, Elizabeth
Explorers. – (Heroes or zeros?) (Atomic)
910.9
A full catalogue record for this book is available
from the British Library.

Acknowledgements

The publishers would like to thank the following for
permission to reproduce photographs: akg-images p.**13**
(bottom); The Art Archive pp. **9** (Museo de la Toree del
Orro Seville/Dagli Orti), **18**, **13** (top) (Musée du Château
de Versailles/Dagli Orti); Bridgeman Art Library pp. **14**
(Christie's Images/Private Collection), **17** (National Gallery
of Victoria, Melbourne, Australia, Gilbee Bequest); Corbis
pp. **5** (top) (Bettmann), **6** (Ralph White), **7** (Bettmann),
10 (Bettmann), **21**, **25** (David Keaton); Getty Images pp.
22 (Hulton Archive), **23** (Time Life Pictures), **26**; Topfoto
(Charles Walker) p. **5** (bottom).

Cover photograph of explorer Captain James Cook
reproduced with permission of Corbis.

The publishers would like to thank Diana Bentley,
Nancy Harris, and Dee Reid for their assistance in the
preparation of this book.

Every effort has been made to contact copyright holders
of any material reproduced in this book. Any omissions
will be rectified in subsequent printings if notice is given
to the publishers.

Fewer than 700 people escaped the sinking *Titanic* in lifeboats.

TITANIC
The World's Largest Liner

WHITE STAR LINE

SOUTHAMPTON ~ NEW YORK
VIA CHERBOURG & QUEENSTOWN

Exciting facts!

The wreck of the *Titanic* was about 4 kilometres (2.5 miles) below the ocean's surface.

People thought the *Titanic* was "unsinkable" when it was launched.

Ballard took 20,000 photos of the *Titanic* wreck.

New rules

In 2003 the British government set up rules to control visits to the *Titanic*. In 2004 the United States agreed to these rules.

Robert Ballard's discovery led other explorers to the Titanic. Some explorers caused damage. They took 6,000 items, including dishes and the ship's bells. Some even offered tours of the sunken ship.

Protecting Titanic

Ballard was upset. He wanted the Titanic to be treated with respect. He felt it should be treated like a graveyard.

Do you think people should explore shipwrecks like the Titanic? Would you? Why or why not?

Ballard gave speeches and wrote a book about his adventure.

Sail To The Americas With Christopher Columbus

In 1492 explorer Christopher Columbus left Spain. He planned to sail around the world to Asia. Columbus was not afraid. His sailors worried about the dangerous voyage.

Land!

On 12 October 1492, they reached an island. The island was in what is now called the West Indies (see the map on page 29). Columbus claimed the island for Spain.

In the **Americas**, Columbus and his crew killed native people. They killed natives who did not help them. They made others **slaves**.

Americas	North and South America and the islands off the coast
slave	person who is owned by someone else

Columbus and 90 men sailed to the Americas in 3 ships. This type of ship was called a caravel.

Exciting facts!

Columbus returned to the West Indies three times in search of gold. He made himself ruler.

This picture is meant to show Columbus landing at San Salvador in the Americas.

Many people think Christopher Columbus was a hero. Dozens of cities, towns, rivers, and schools in the United States are named after him. Columbus Day, a US holiday, is also named after him.

Hero or zero?

However, some people do not **celebrate** Columbus. They say that he took land that belonged to others. Millions of people lived in the **Americas** before Columbus landed. They had their own languages and ways of living. They had their own governments (leaders). Columbus did not respect the people or their ways. He harmed them.

Do you think Columbus was a hero? Why or why not?

celebrate   honour

Search For Inca Gold With Francisco Pizarro

In the 1500s, Spanish explorers followed Columbus's route to the **Americas**. They were looking for gold. One explorer heard stories of a golden **empire** to the south. His name was Francisco Pizarro.

On to Peru

In 1531 Pizarro and 180 men left what is now Panama (see the map on page 29). They travelled along the coast of South America. They went as far as present-day Peru. There, they met Atahualpa. He was an **Inca** ruler. Pizarro gave Atahualpa a Bible (holy book). Atahualpa tossed it aside. Pizarro was insulted. He and his men attacked.

empire	kingdom
Inca	people of ancient Peru

Pizarro dreamed of Inca gold.

Exciting facts!

Inca objects, such as this gold statue, eventually became part of museum displays.

Pizarro and his men fought the Incas.

Francisco Pizarro melted **Inca** gold and took it back to Spain. Thanks to Pizarro, Spain became a rich country. Pizarro introduced the Spanish language and Spanish customs to South America. He **founded** the city of Lima in present-day Peru. Some people consider Pizarro a hero. He claimed this new land and all its treasure for his country, Spain.

The other side

However, others say that Pizarro was not a hero. He captured and killed Inca rulers for gold and silver. He forced the people to be **slaves** and follow orders. He stole their treasures. Pizarro destroyed a great kingdom.

What do you think about Pizarro? Is he a hero? Why or why not?

found   begin or set up something, such as a city

Explore The South Pacific With James Cook

English explorer Captain James Cook set sail for Australia in 1768 (see the map on page 29). Unlike Pizarro, he was not searching for gold. He wanted to learn about the islands of the South Pacific.

Cook cares

During this time in history, many sailors got **scurvy**. Their teeth fell out and their skin and hair dried out. Some died. Not Cook's crew. Cook took care of his men. He made them eat foods rich in vitamin C. They ate lemons, limes, and **sauerkraut**. No one got sick.

sauerkraut	chopped cabbage soaked in cabbage juice and salt
scurvy	disease caused by lack of vitamin C

Cook landed at Botany Bay, Australia, in 1770. He was the first European to reach this bay.

Exciting facts!

Captain Cook took scientist Joseph Banks along on his trip. Banks studied plants, birds, and native people.

Captain Cook was killed on the beach at Kealakekua by angry Hawaiians.

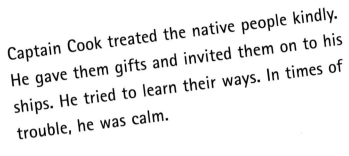

Captain Cook treated the native people kindly. He gave them gifts and invited them on to his ships. He tried to learn their ways. In times of trouble, he was calm.

Cook changes

Things changed during Cook's third trip. He travelled to Hawaii (see map on page 29). When some Hawaiians stole a small boat, Cook exploded in anger. Cook was killed in the battle that followed.

Everyone agrees that Cook was a good captain to his men. He was also the first explorer to visit Hawaii. But losing his temper cost him his life.

Is he a hero? Why or why not?

What happened?

Why did Cook change and lose his temper? No one knows.

Fly Over The North Pole With Richard Byrd

US explorer Richard Byrd looked out of his aeroplane window. He could see the **North Pole** (see the map on page 29). He wanted to be the first person to fly over it. Then, his plane sputtered. It was leaking oil. Could he make it?

Hero?

On 10 May 1926, newspapers reported that Byrd had flown over the North Pole. He had made it! People cheered, held parades, and gave him medals.

Three years later Byrd was the first to fly over the **South Pole**. The date was 29 November 1929. He explored Antarctica for several months.

North Pole	**northernmost point of Earth**
South Pole	**southernmost point of Earth**

Byrd was given a hero's welcome in New York, USA.

Byrd brought emperor penguins back from Antarctica.

dogsled   **sledge pulled by dogs**

Thanks to Richard Byrd, explorers began to use aeroplanes to visit the **North** and **South Poles**. Before this, people had used **dogsleds**. Aeroplane travel was faster and warmer. Byrd's reports of his explorations helped people better understand the North and South Poles.

Liar?

However, some people think Byrd lied about flying over the North Pole. A diary was found in 1996. It seems to prove that Byrd turned back 241 kilometres (150 miles) before reaching the North Pole.

Does it matter if Byrd really flew over the North Pole? How important is it to tell the truth? Do you think Byrd was a hero? Why or why not?

Byrd flew this plane on his North Pole adventures.

CLIMB MOUNT EVEREST WITH DAN MAZUR

Climbing the world's tallest mountain is an adventure. Many explorers try. Not everyone succeeds.

Danger!

More than 2,000 people have tried to climb Mount Everest. It is in southern Asia (see the map on page 29). About 185 people have died doing so. When someone dies on Everest, the body is left there.

On 15 May 2006, David Sharp became sick as he climbed up Everest. Forty climbers passed by him. Stopping to help someone on Everest can be dangerous. Sharp died.

Exciting facts!

Mount Everest is 8,850 metres (29,035 feet) high.

Climbers must face ice, cold, and high winds to get to the top of Mount Everest.

Lincoln Hall stands in front of Mount Everest after his rescue.

Ten days later another climber, Lincoln Hall, became sick. His friends thought he was dead. They left him on the mountain. They went on.

Dead or alive?

The next day, climber Dan Mazur passed the dead body of David Sharp. Then, he saw Lincoln Hall on a nearby cliff. He stopped. Was Hall dead or alive? Mazur stopped to find out. Two other climbers passed by. Mazur asked them to help. They said no.

Mazur took Hall back down the mountain. Hall suffered **frostbite**, but he lived!

Why did Mazur help? Why did others pass by? What would you have done? Why?

frostbite   **injury caused by freezing**

WHO IS A HERO? YOU DECIDE

If you could go on one of these amazing journeys, which would you choose? Why?

Compare the explorers on the timeline below. Who do you think is the greatest hero? Why?

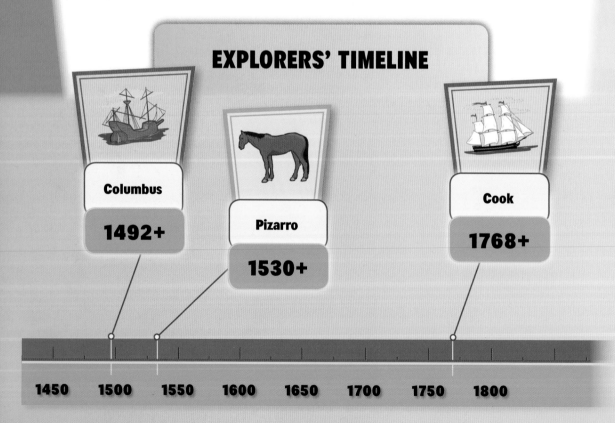

EXPLORERS' TIMELINE

Columbus

1492+

Pizarro

1530+

Cook

1768+

1450   1500   1550   1600   1650   1700   1750   1800

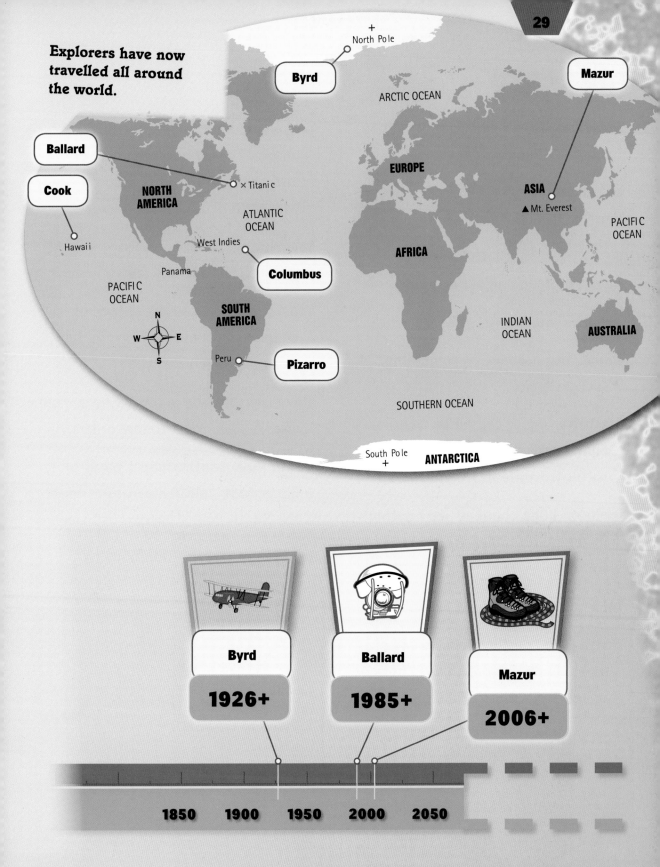

Explorers have now travelled all around the world.

North Pole +

Byrd

ARCTIC OCEAN

Mazur

Ballard

× Titanic

EUROPE

ASIA

▲ Mt. Everest

Cook

NORTH AMERICA

ATLANTIC OCEAN

PACIFIC OCEAN

Hawaii

West Indies

AFRICA

Columbus

Panama

PACIFIC OCEAN

SOUTH AMERICA

INDIAN OCEAN

AUSTRALIA

N
W E
S

Peru

Pizarro

SOUTHERN OCEAN

South Pole +   ANTARCTICA

Byrd
1926+

Ballard
1985+

Mazur
2006+

1850   1900   1950   2000   2050

Glossary

Americas North and South America and the islands off the coast

celebrate honour. Celebrated people are well-liked for the things that they have done.

dogsled sledge pulled by dogs

empire kingdom

found begin or set up something, such as a city

frostbite injury caused by freezing. Fingers, toes, ears, and noses can suffer frostbite in freezing weather.

iceberg huge chunk of ice floating in the ocean. Ships must watch out for icebergs.

Inca people of ancient Peru

North Pole northernmost point of Earth. Early explorers used dogsleds to reach the North Pole.

passenger liner ship built to carry people. The *Titanic* was the world's largest passenger liner when it was built.

sauerkraut chopped cabbage soaked in cabbage juice and salt

scurvy disease caused by lack of vitamin C. People with scurvy feel weak and bleed easily.

slave person who is owned by someone else. A slave must follow orders.

South Pole southernmost point of Earth. Very cold temperatures make the South Pole a dangerous place.

submarine special ship built to go underwater

Want to Know More?

Books

✷ *Explorers of North America*, Brendan January (Children's Press, 2001)

✷ *Explorers: Pioneers Who Broke New Boundaries*, Richard Platt (Dorling Kindersley, 2001)

✷ *The Picture History of Great Explorers*, Gillian Clements (Frances Lincoln, 2005)

Websites

✷ www.encyclopedia-titanic.org
Visit this site to learn more about the *Titanic* including crew and passenger lists, deck plans, biographies, and much more!

✷ www.yahooligans.com
Type "Christopher Columbus" or "James Cook" into this search engine and follow the links to find out more about these two famous explorers.

If you liked this Atomic book, why don't you try these...?

Index

Notes for adults
Use the following questions to guide children towards identifying features of discussion text:

Can you give an example of summary on page 7?
Can you give an example of a statement of the issue from page 11?
Can you find examples of different opinions on page 15?
Can you find an example of a logical connective on page 23?
Can you find examples of present tense language on page 23?